Doing Drugs

Alcohol and other drug education for Christian groups and organisations

Martin Perry, BA
Illustrator: Andy Robb

25(f) Copperfield St
London SE1 0EN

Tel: *0171 928 0848* (24 hrs)
Fax: *0171 401 3477*

Contents

Biblical quotes have been taken from the 'Good News Bible' or the 'New International Version'.

Designed by C A Senior
Printed by CPO Print
Published by Hope UK, 25(f) Copperfield St, London SE1 0EN
Registered Charity No. 1044475

© Hope UK 1996

ISBN 0 946507 30 9

A QUESTION of bALANCE

Exercise, healthy eating and sleep are important in maintaining life's balance. People do not always realise that the mind affects the body and vice versa. If people are continually fed up they are likely to develop physical symptoms. Emotional stress can bring on headaches, skin rashes and other physical problems. Falling in love sometimes makes people lose their appetite! Similarly, something physical can affect the mind - having a broken arm or leg or being confined to bed can affect the way you feel. Substance use (the non-medical or social use of drugs and solvents) will affect the health of our bodies and minds.

Thoughts, feelings and beliefs

Our feelings spring from our minds where we store what we believe. Most of the time we do things thinking we know what will result from our actions; but sometimes we do not appreciate all the facts. Many people know nothing about engines and yet happily drive cars because experience says that they will work.

However, there are also many things that people disagree about although they start from the same evidence. Religious belief is an obvious example - some people believe in God and some do not. Some are Christians and others follow different faiths. When confronted with no obvious right answer it is important to be able to use one's mind to judge what to believe. Most people know that substance use is related to a great deal of misery and yet millions of people use one or more drugs every day. Why do you think this is so?

God's love

Christians believe that Jesus came in order that we might have *"life in all its fullness"* (John Ch. 10 v 10). He wants us to enjoy life and to get the most we can out of it. To do that we must give our hearts to Him and allow Him to direct our lives.

Our bodies are the temple of the Holy Spirit and should be kept healthy and fit for His service. (See 1 Corinthians Ch. 6 vs 19-20.)

Nobody feels brilliant all the time. Life is full of ups and downs; but if our life is in balance we can cope. Sometimes we can feel very alone or unimportant. Perhaps we even think that nobody cares about us. In God's eyes each of us is very significant. Jesus used a powerful example to show how much God cares for each of us: *"even the very hairs of your head are all numbered. So don't be afraid; you are worth more than many sparrows."* (Matthew Ch. 10 vs 30-31)

Positive lifestyles

Many people are worried about drugs. A lot of money is spent helping people with problems and providing education to inform others about the risks. But millions of people still choose to use substances because they want the mind-altering or physical effects.

The Bible gives important lifestyle guidelines. God asks us to live out a life that is pleasing to Him. *"You were taught, with regard to your former way of life to put off your old self, which is being corrupted by its deceitful desires."* (Ephesians Ch. 4 v 22) Paul is telling us to leave behind our old habits and ways and to live out our new life. In living out that life, people see a difference. Sometimes

3

we don't even need to say anything! Actions will speak louder than words.

Knowing the facts about drugs, and the effects they can have on us, should help us consider whether these substances encourage a lifestyle Jesus wants us to live.

Self -assessment questions

1. List 3 things that make you feel good and 3 things that make you feel down. Think about how you cope with these feelings.
2. In God's eyes why is each of us important?
3. Does 1 Corinthians Ch. 6 vs 19 & 20 say anything about drug taking?
4. List some situations where you have been a good or bad example.

Project idea

Design a short questionnaire to discover people's attitudes towards alcohol, tobacco and other drugs. Short yes/no questions are best - e.g.
    Do you drink alcohol? Yes/No
    Should smoking be allowed on church premises? Yes/No
Decide who the questionnaire is to be used with, e.g. members of your church. Record all the information and make an attractive display of your results.

World Scene

Whose world is it anyway?

"The world and all that is in it belong to the Lord? The earth and all who live in it are his." (Psalm 24 v 1)

We live in a world which has many different cultures, rich with wildlife and breathtaking in its variety of landscape. At the same time millions of people live in poverty, the environment is being damaged, wildlife is being destroyed, wars are being fought and drug trafficking is **big business**.

Global responsibility

World issues can be overwhelming.
Individually we can't save the tiger or solve the problems of world poverty. **But** if everybody said this nothing would happen.

Whose responsibility?

There were four people named Everybody, Somebody, Anybody and Nobody.

There was an important job to be done, and Everybody was asked to do it.

Anybody could have done it, but Nobody did it.

Somebody got angry about that because it was Everybody's job.

Everybody thought Anybody could do it, but Nobody realised that Everybody wouldn't do it.

It ended up that Everybody blamed Somebody when Nobody did what Anybody could have done.

Individual importance

You are important where you are. What you do will have an influence on others around you even if it is not immediately obvious. You may be a shy person or an extrovert. We all have different things that we are good at and all these differences affect the groups to which we belong.

"So then the eye cannot say to the hand, 'I don't need you!' nor can the head say to the feet, 'Well, I don't need you!' On the contrary, we can't do without the parts of the body that seem to be weaker . . . so there is no division in the body, but all its different parts have the same concern for one another. If one part of the body suffers, all the other parts suffer with it; if one part is praised, all the other parts share its happiness." (Extracts from 1 Corinthians Ch. 12 vs 21-26)

Belonging

As well as belonging to small groups like our family, club or school, we also belong in the community where we live. Individuals can and do make a difference. Some get involved by being elected on to the Council, others have taken direct action where they live and cut crime and drug taking by setting up neighbourhood watch schemes. Some get everyone to work together to improve their local environment.

No individual can take on **all** the cares of the world; but **you** can care and get involved. In fact we each have a responsibility to do so.

When God created the world He put human beings in charge of all His creation. When He did this He did not mean that we could do as we wanted; but rather that it was our responsibility. (See Genesis Ch. 1 vs 26-31)

Drugs for food?

Some drugs are 'artificial'. They are chemically made while others grow 'naturally'. Mistakenly, the latter are sometimes thought to be automatically 'good' because they are 'natural'. For instance, heroin is made from the opium poppy which grows in parts of Asia. Heroin is a strong painkiller and has medicinal use; but it can also be abused. It sounds easy to say "let's wipe out the unregistered opium poppy fields and solve the heroin abuse problem in the west"; but it is not quite as simple as that. Many of the people who grow the opium poppy are very poor and they can get more money for their poppies than if they grow food. If they couldn't grow their poppies they might not be able to afford to grow another crop and they would not be able to buy the seeds to grow their own food and their family would suffer.

Of course, the price increases many times as the heroin passes through the hands of the drug traffickers who refine the raw opium and import it to Europe, the suppliers who act as wholesalers and the dealers who sell it illegally on the street. Along the way a great deal of money is made; but not by the farmer who grew the poppies. Something similar happens with cocaine which originates in South America. Remember that there are some very wealthy, powerful and ruthless people involved in the drug business, all out to make money at the expense of their customers!

Take action

It takes time and effort to be involved and to take action; but it's worth it. Caring for our planet which God has created for us and preventing its destruction are vitally important. The illegal drug 'industry' can damage both the physical and the social environment.

We can all help at our local level by promoting positive ways to live and work together to reduce the sale of illegal drugs in our community. At the same time we can work towards a better and fairer world which would help to eliminate the drug criminals who make fortunes at other people's and the world's expense.

Even the tobacco industry has significant effects on our environment (See Module 3)

Self-assessment questions

1. How would you answer someone who said "I can't do anything about the world's problems"?
2. In 1 Corinthians Ch. 12 vs 21-26 what does Paul say about working together?
3. Explain how heroin gets from the opium poppy to the user in the UK.

Project idea

Improve your local community. Research good and bad aspects of your area. Draw up a plan for improvement. Who would need to be involved to put these plans into action?

Smoking

Smoking tobacco is a form of taking drugs. The drug found in cigarettes is nicotine and is a stimulant drug - this means that it stimulates the Central Nervous System (i.e. the body's control system).

When people smoke they fill their lungs with all sorts of toxic gases and irritants. The two main ones are carbon monoxide and tar. These reduce the amount of oxygen that enters the blood, and the heart becomes weaker. Smoking greatly increases the risks of suffering from heart disease and lung cancer. Other cancers are now found to have a definite link with smoking, e.g. gastric and cervical cancers.

Deaths related to tobacco are approximately 111,000 a year in the UK alone. One in every six deaths among adults aged 35 and over is due to smoking.

(No Smoking Day 1996)

People do stop smoking - approximately 12 million adults or 26% of the population are ex-smokers

(Office of Population & Census Surveys 1994)

For a young person 35 seems a long way away and many ignore the health risks: 10% of boys and 13% of girls (aged 11-15) are regular smokers.

(OPCS 1994)

The law restricts sales of cigarettes to over 16's; but 71% of 11-15 year olds who tried to buy cigarettes in the past year claim never to have been refused.

(OPCS 1994)

So the law doesn't seem to be working and despite the campaigns asking "Who wants to kiss an ashtray?" or "Do you want yellow nicotine stained fingers?" the pressure to smoke seems to be greater.

- Children who smoke tend to mix with other smokers. 75% of regular smokers aged 9-15 mix with a circle of friends who smoke.

(Health Education Authority 1992)

- 68% of young people in England aged 11-15 in 1993 will have tried smoking by the time they are 16.

(OPCS 1994)

"It's my life and I can smoke if I want to." Wrong!

- Breathing other people's smoke is called passive, involuntary or second-hand smoking. It has also been found that passive smoking aggravates asthma. Chronic coughs and phlegm are more frequent among children of parents who smoke and glue ear in children is associated with passive smoking.

(No Smoking Day 1996)

- Children of parents who smoke inhale nicotine in amounts equivalent to their actively smoking 60–150 cigarettes a year, thus putting them at increased risk of developing cancer as they get older.

(Royal College of Physicians 1992)

- Women who smoke during pregnancy have a 27% higher chance of miscarriage. They are twice as likely to experience premature labour. They have babies who are lighter by an average of 200g.

(Royal College of Physicians 1992)

- In England about 16 million working days are lost each year due to absence caused by chronic bronchitis, emphysema and asthma.

(Department of Social Security 1993)

- It is estimated that the cost of treating diseases caused by smoking is £500 million a year.

(Department of Health)

The environment

Smokers may not realise the effects on the rest of the world.

- Growing tobacco means that less land is available for food crops. While some food is grown between crops of tobacco, it has been estimated that ten to twenty million people could be fed by food crops grown instead of tobacco.

(Barry M 1991)

- A modern cigarette manufacturing machine uses four miles of paper per hour.

(Chapman & Leng 1991)

Tobacco takes up 1.5% of world agricultural export trade. In some poor countries tobacco is grown to provide money to pay off debts to wealthy countries. This means that vital land for growing food is wasted and starvation is one result of this process.

The tobacco plant draws nutrients out of the soil quicker than other crops. After several seasons of growing tobacco the soil is useless and other plants cannot grow in it.

In addition, each crop of tobacco is sprayed with sixteen doses of pesticide. These can pollute drinking water and kill animals apart from the insects which they are designed to kill.

Advertising

Tobacco companies are now diverting their advertising budget to third world countries. More and more people who are not aware of the dangers of smoking are being encouraged to spend their money on cigarettes. The effects on the individuals and the health care needed in these countries will not become apparent for some years to come.

Stay smoke free

The best advice is not to start smoking. Your clothes won't smell, your breath will be fresher and you will be reducing the risk of future health problems. Smoking is not a cool thing to do. Nicotine is a very addictive substance and it can be hard to stop once you have started.

Why not break the habit?

If you do smoke, or have a friend or family member who does, it is a good idea to have an action plan. Here are some practical ideas on why it is best to stop and how to do it.

Seven-day count down to Stopping Smoking

7 days to go . . .

Make sure you're stopping because YOU want to. Check your own reasons against this list, then think of your own. Keep your list handy over the next few months.

When I've stopped, I'll . . .

be fitter;

save money;

breathe more easily;

be less likely to have a heart attack;

have less chance of getting lung cancer;

have fresher smelling breath, hair and clothes;

have more chance of having a healthy baby;

set a good example to my family and friends.

6 dAys to go . . .

Try to understand your smoking habits. Smoking is often linked to certain situations and times of day. To break these links you may need to change your habits for a while. So if you always have a cigarette when you have a cup of tea or coffee, try having a fruit juice instead. Plan in advance how you will cope with difficult situations.

5 dAys to go . . .

Tell your family and friends you've decided to stop and the date on which you'll quit. Ask for their understanding and support - the more encouragement you get, the more successful you'll be. If you want some friendly help and advice on stopping, call the smokers' helpline (0800 00 22 00).

4 dAys to go . . .

Think about how you will keep your mind off cigarettes for the next few weeks. You'll need to keep your hands and your mind busy. Now could be the time to try a new hobby.

3 dAys to go . . .

Stock up on nibbles - when you've stopped you may find it helpful to chew sugar-free gum, fruit or raw vegetables.

2 days to go . . .

Learn a relaxation technique to help relieve stress. Find out about exercise classes in your area or get involved in one of your church activities.

1 day to go . . .

Now you're ready to stop smoking. Before you go to bed throw away everything to do with smoking - your cigarettes, lighters and ashtrays.

(Based on No Smoking Day advice 1996)

Finally, think of all the money you'll save! You'll be amazed how quickly a cigarette money jar will fill up. Before long you'll be able to get that CD you want or go on a new clothes spending spree.

Don't forget – if you smoke cigarettes you are much more likely to try other illegal drugs. A Mori poll found that 54% of 14/15 year old smokers had tried other drugs, but only 2% of non-smokers had done so.

Self-assessment questions

a) What is the effect of nicotine?

b) What is the cost to the Health Service of treating smoking-related diseases?

c) What is passive smoking? Why is it a problem?

d) Why is the tobacco industry not helpful to poorer countries?

e) What would be the benefits of stopping smoking?

Project idea

Use a cassette recorder to work out and record a short education spot on smoking, using interviews with smokers and non-smokers etc.

Drinking

Alcohol - Britain's Favourite Drug

"Alcohol causes ten times as much damage to the young compared with other drugs."

Professor Sir Leslie Turnberg, Royal College of Physicians.

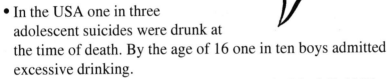

• A thousand young people under 16 need intensive hospital treatment every year in the UK as a result of alcohol use.

• In the USA one in three adolescent suicides were drunk at the time of death. By the age of 16 one in ten boys admitted excessive drinking.

(Exeter University Schools Health Education Unit)

• 65% of 14-15 year olds admitted to being drunk at least once in the last year.

(Alcohol and Offending Research Unit, University of Manchester)

What is alcohol?

Alcohol is the chemical C_2H_5OH and is found in methylated and surgical spirits, industrial solvents, thermometers, paint stripper, cosmetics and after-shave lotions – and in drinks!

Let's take a closer look at alcohol. Alcohol is absorbed into the bloodstream and it interferes with normal brain activity. We start to feel different . . . We think more slowly . . . But we feel that we are better at doing things than we really are, e.g. better drivers, more interesting, better people. Alcohol temporarily alters the way our mind works.

The healthy drinker?

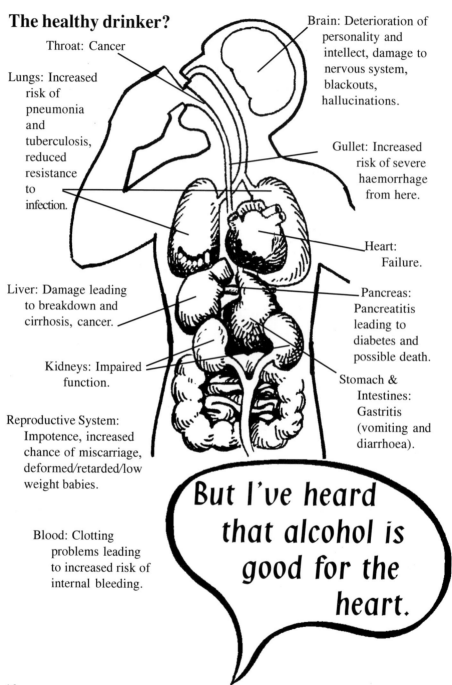

Throat: Cancer

Lungs: Increased risk of pneumonia and tuberculosis, reduced resistance to infection.

Brain: Deterioration of personality and intellect, damage to nervous system, blackouts, hallucinations.

Gullet: Increased risk of severe haemorrhage from here.

Heart: Failure.

Liver: Damage leading to breakdown and cirrhosis, cancer.

Kidneys: Impaired function.

Reproductive System: Impotence, increased chance of miscarriage, deformed/retarded/low weight babies.

Blood: Clotting problems leading to increased risk of internal bleeding.

Pancreas: Pancreatitis leading to diabetes and possible death.

Stomach & Intestines: Gastritis (vomiting and diarrhoea).

But I've heard that alcohol is good for the heart.

In the Bible Paul advised Timothy to take a little wine for his stomach's sake. (1 Timothy Ch. 5 v 23)

Research has shown that low consumption may reduce the risk of coronary heart disease for middle-aged men and women; but are the possible benefits greater than the potential risks? Heavier levels of drinking can increase blood pressure and lead to heart failure.

"There is no minimum threshold below which alcohol can be consumed without any risk."

(Hans Emblad, World Health Organisation)

"Don't you know that your body is the temple of the Holy Spirit who lives in you . . . so use your bodies for God's glory."

(1 Corinthians Ch. 6 v 19-20)

Life is like a pair of scales – can you keep in balance? (See Module 1)

Many people consume alcohol without any apparent problems. As this chart shows there are 'good' as well as 'bad' effects — but do the bad outweigh the good?

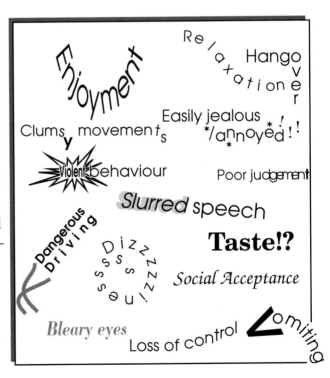

Drinking through the centuries

Throughout history people have used substances to give them instant pleasure. Alcohol is one of the drugs used for this purpose. Wine (i.e. fermented grape juice) was used very early in human existence, particularly in the Mediterranean area. However, not all grapes were made into wine. Fresh fruit juice was drunk and many grapes were dried into raisins.

Distillation was invented in the 8th century - a process by which alcohol vapour is drawn off when beers or wines are heated to just below the boiling point of water. This made possible the production of much stronger alcoholic drinks known as 'spirits' (gin, whisky, etc.) and 'liqueurs' (Tia Maria, Cointreau etc.).

The following description, written over two thousand years ago, clearly describes the effects of alcohol:

> *"Show me someone who drinks too much, who has to try out some new drink, and I will show you someone miserable and sorry for himself, always causing trouble and always complaining. His eyes are bloodshot, and he has bruises that could be avoided. Don't let wine tempt you, even though it is rich red, though it sparkles in the cup, and it goes down smoothly. The next morning you will feel as if you have been bitten by a poisonous snake. Weird sights will appear before your eyes, and you will not be able to think or speak clearly. You will feel as if you are out on the ocean, seasick, swinging high up in the rigging of a tossing ship. 'I must have been hit,' you will say; 'I must have been beaten up, but I don't remember it. Why can't I wake up? I need another drink'."*

(Proverbs 23 v 29-35)

Alcohol is related to all these problems

88% criminal damage

78% assaults

33% 15 year old boys get into fights after drinking

30% of divorces

19% drownings

40% domestic violence

33% adolescent suicides (USA)

30% child abuse cases

LESH STRY THISH ROOM! HIC!

and there is a strong link between drinking habits, sexually transmitted diseases and the HIV virus.

Sensible shopping?

Go into any supermarket or off-licence and you will see there are rows and rows of different alcoholic drinks. Distilled drinks like whisky, gin and vodka have a high concentration of alcohol, but are usually served in small quantities. Some beers and ciders can be over twice as strong as a 'standard' drink and there is now a whole range of alcoholic lemonades, colas, sodas and tonics which disguise the alcoholic taste.

Despite a voluntary advertising code which says that alcoholic drinks should not appeal to young people or show success in relationships and sport, many drink adverts are popular with young people and children.

There is an argument that if children are taught to drink 'sensibly' then they will not have problems with alcohol. Unfortunately many young people drink for the drug effect, to get drunk, because this is their image of having a good time – they don't want to be sensible. Also, everyone who has a drink problem started as a social or sensible drinker. Accurate information is necessary in order to make an informed decision about drinking.

To drink or not to drink, that is the question . . .

"I'm free to do what I like!"

Jesus said: *"If the Son sets you free you will be really free"*. (John Ch. 8 v 36) What does it mean to be really free? Is it a freedom to harm yourself or others?

20

People whose lives depend on their next shot of alcohol, nicotine or other drugs face an 'imprisonment' which is often unseen and unrealised.

Freedom is something to be treasured. Caring for others is a fine principle to live by. People need to think about their own actions and make positive decisions.

The Bible offers guidelines for us to follow.

- It condemns getting drunk and gives examples where some people drank in moderation and others abstained.
- Jesus almost certainly would have drunk the weak wine of his day. But in those days a mildly alcoholic drink may have been safer than the often polluted water.
- Being drunk in charge of a donkey was a lot less dangerous than driving a car under the influence.
- There were no super strong beers or spirits being heavily promoted by a sophisticated advertising industry.
- Neither were there millions suffering from drug abuse.
- Jewish society insisted on a very controlled use of alcohol.

Life today is very different from first century Palestine.

In today's world everyone needs to consider the option of being alcohol-free. This is not always easy in a society where alcohol is automatically used on so many occasions. However, the decision to be alcohol-free is really positive, not only for ourselves, but also as an example to others. Paul said, *"If what I eat (or drink) causes my brother to fall into sin, I will never eat meat (drink) again, so that I will not cause him to fall."* (1 Corinthians Ch. 8 v 13)

The Law

"Everything is permissible – but not everything is beneficial."

(1 Corinthians Ch. 10 v 23)

- Paul warns that while all things may be lawful – not all things are helpful.
- Not all things build us up as people or bring glory to God.
- A drug does not have to be illegal to be dangerous.
- Alcohol is legal but it can still be dangerous.

Self-assessment questions

1. Why is alcohol thought to be ten times more harmful to young people than other drugs?
2. Although a very small amount of alcohol may reduce the risk of heart diseaseamong some older people, why might it be better not to drink?
3. Write down all the effects of alcohol. Decide which are good and bad ones.
4. Explain in your own words whether the Bible says we are free to harm ourselves or others.

Project idea

Put together a scrap book of local and/or national newspaper cuttings on alcohol. Comment on whether they are for or against drinking alcohol. You could also do a survey of alcohol adverts, analysing each one and trying to identify the selling points.

OtHeR DRUGS

What are drugs?

They are **substances which alter the way the body works.**

All drugs have side effects; but used medically the benefits usually outweigh the risks. Some users of illegal drugs believe that what they see as the positive effect of the drugs is worth the risk.

The misuse of drugs is often called 'substance abuse'. This is not just limited to illegal substances like heroin, cocaine, crack and cannabis. Alcohol and nicotine are the two drugs associated with **most** of the substance problems in the UK. Solvent abuse (sniffing glue, aerosols and other 'volatile substances') is prevalent in some areas. Chemically produced drugs like LSD (acid), ecstasy and amphetamine sulphate (speed, whizz) are also used.

Substance abuse does not stop with the social use of drugs for 'enjoyment'. Doctors correctly prescribe drugs like Valium, Librium and Temazepam (called Benzodiazepines) for stress and insomnia (sleeplessness). Unfortunately, patients may come to depend on these drugs without ever solving the problems that cause the stress in the first place. Other people will use alcohol or other drugs to relieve stress without bothering to consult a doctor.

Drugs are fun

Just because something is enjoyable doesn't mean that it is good for you or will not cause you harm. What seems to be fun and exciting can end up causing problems for a very long time – or even death.

Freedom stealers

Drug dealers are in business to make money. They exploit young people because they are easy targets. They encourage 'friendship' dealing which makes it seem all right. In the search for fun and excitement, people don't always see the dangers. There is no quality control for illegal drugs and no guarantee about purity. Other substances in the illegal drug could be something more harmful than the drug itself.

Ecstasy (MDMA)

Users say it gives them increased energy and 'spacey' feelings of well-being. But use can lead to fatigue, weight loss and feelings of anxiety and depression. "Ecstasy is a toxic substance" (Dr John Henry, National Poisons Unit). It can cause the body to overheat, especially if used when dancing, and may cause liver or kidney damage. Pure ecstasy is dangerous. It has caused some deaths. The advice to drink lots of water also carries a risk because some people have died from drinking too much!

Amphetamines (Speed, Whizz or Sulph)

These give a rush or buzz and may cause nervous excitability, sleeplessness, agitation, talkativeness, aggressiveness, lack of appetite and seemingly unlimited energy. Other effects may include a dry mouth and thirst, sweating, palpitations, increased blood pressure, nausea, sickness, headaches, dizziness and tremors. Effects usually wear off after 3 or 4 hours when the user suddenly becomes tired, irritable, depressed or unable to concentrate. Feelings of confusion, persecution or violence can follow. There can be a strong desire to continue taking the drug and the need to increase the amounts for the same sensations.

Ice is a type of amphetamine which can be smoked. Crystals can contain 90% - 100% of the pure drug.

Cocaine (Coke, Charlie, Happy Dust, Rock)

Cocaine is made from the leaf of the coca plant grown in South America. Sniffing or injecting cocaine gives a period of exhilaration and euphoria, which can be followed by feelings of agitation, anxiety or fear. Large doses cause sleeplessness, hallucinations, tremors and convulsions.

Crack is a smokeable form of cocaine which gets the drug into the brain very quickly. The "high" is very short-lived and may wear off within 12 minutes. Continued use can cause an enormous compulsive craving for the drug.

LSD (Trips, Acid, Tabs)

LSD was discovered in 1943 by a Swiss Chemist. It causes hallucinations by interfering with the brain's filtering mechanisms which help distinguish what is real from what is imagination. This can cause people to "feel" colours or "taste" smells. Trips can include a complete loss of emotional control, disorientation, depression, dizziness and panic. Accidents may occur whilst under the influence of LSD.

Magic Mushrooms have hallucinogenic properties similar to LSD.

Heroin (H, Smack, Junk)

Heroin is made from Opium. For a long time Opium and its derivatives have been used to relieve pain. Heroin can be smoked, inhaled (chasing the dragon) or injected. All methods give a high but the side effects damage health and cause addiction. There is no quality control. Illegal or street drugs are often cut (mixed) with other nasty substances like scouring powder. At the other extreme, there is a real risk of taking a fatal overdose. Injecting also has a high risk of infection. Sharing needles is a high risk activity in relation to contracting the HIV virus and/or hepatitis B.

Solvents

Almost any household or other substance which gives off vapour can be abused. Since the sale of glue is now quite well controlled in the shops, aerosols, gases and fuels have become more commonly used. Solvents tend to give a 'buzz' which will come quickly and be something like a drunk feeling. Generally, the effects wear off faster than those of alcohol. Sniffing is a high risk activity and it is estimated that first time users account for 1 in 4 of the deaths caused by solvents.

Cannabis (Dope, Weed, Grass, etc)

Cannabis is the most easily obtained illegal drug in Britain. It is usually sold in its herbal form (dried leaves and flowers) or as blocks of resin scraped from the plant. THC (delta-1-tetrahydrocannabinol) is what gives Cannabis its effects. THC is absorbed into the fatty tissues of the body, such as the brain, and it is only slowly released into the blood stream.

Why not use Cannabis?

There is a risk to health . . . cannabis is at least four times as likely to cause cancer as tobacco.

There is a risk to yourself . . . under the influence of cannabis co-ordination and judgement will be affected.

There is a risk to your emotions . . . cannabis affects the ability to think properly. Making important decisions could be disastrous.

There is a risk to your sociability . . . cannabis affects attitude and interest.

There is a risk to your intellect . . . cannabis affects short-term memory.

There is a risk to your inner self . . . regular or heavy use of cannabis can cause mental problems.

Cannabis affects the whole person, physically, psychologically, socially and spiritually.

You cannot have a real spiritual experience under the influence of Cannabis. A real meeting with God requires living in the real world - not hiding from reality. *"Live as free people."* (1 Peter Ch. 2 v 16)

Free to choose

- Liberty for all is important and we should jealously guard our individual freedom of choice.

- But one person's freedom can become another person's prison. This is particularly so in the case of alcohol or other drug use.

- For the drug dependent person there is little freedom of choice.

- Across the world, millions and millions of people are literally enslaved by drug use.

- Many occasional drug users believe they're in control and think that 'it won't happen to me'; but drug use is a bit like gambling — it could be you!

- The most positive example is to be drug-free, to show that drugs are **not** necessary for a good time.

Can each of us do our bit to help create a world free from the abuse of drugs?

Self-assessment questions

1. What is a drug?
2. What type of drugs are Amphetamines and Cocaine?
3. Give at least 5 reasons why Cannabis should not be used.
4. Why have Ecstasy users been told to drink water? Why does this carry risks?
5. Explain the phrase "One person's freedom can become another person's prison".

Project idea

Find out all you can about Cannabis. ('Take Dope . . .' available from Hope UK is a good resource.) Present your findings for and against the legalisation of this drug. You could put on a debate.

Knowing the facts about drugs and the effects they can have on us should make us consider whether these substances encourage a lifestyle Jesus wants us to live.

Would Jesus take drugs?

OTHER RESOURCES

Doing Drugs **contains 5 Modules which can be used singly or in any combination. They are best used as part of a planned drug education programme.**

Also available for purchase:

– **A separate pack of brief leaders' notes with photocopiable multi-choice questions and answers.**

– **Certificates of achievement for use with the above question papers.**

We strongly recommend our manual "How to do Drugs" for practical activity ideas.

A free catalogue detailing other literature, posters, and services available from:

Hope UK
25(f) Copperfield St
London SE1 0EN

Tel: *0171 928 0848* (24 hrs)
Fax: *0171 401 3477*